Monty and Rose Nest at Montrose

Tamima Itani

Illustrations by Anna-Maria Crum

Dedication

The mere existence of Great Lakes Piping Plovers today is the result of decades of efforts by the Great Lakes Piping Plover Conservation Team, supported by scores of volunteers around the Great Lakes and on the Piping Plover wintering grounds. This book is dedicated to every person who has stepped up to ensure their future through research, habitat conservation, monitoring of nest and chicks, and advocacy, making it possible for all to continue marveling at these magnificent, endearing, spunky little shorebirds.

The Montrose Beach Dunes provided a suitable nesting habitat thanks to years of conservation work by its steward Leslie Borns, the dunes volunteers, and the Chicago Park District. The nesting effort succeeded through oversight of Brad Semel (IDNR), Louise Clemency (F&WS), and Dr. Francesca Cuthbert (University of Minnesota). Nearly 200 dedicated and loving volunteers, led by the Illinois Ornithological Society, Chicago Ornithological Society, and Chicago Audubon Society, stood guard over nest and chicks from sunrise to sunset for 13 consecutive weeks. Monty and Rose rewarded us with the most precious of gifts, two chicks fledged in Chicago and in Cook County for the first time in 71 years.

This book is dedicated to all of you who made it possible.

One hundred percent of the net proceeds from the sale of this book will be donated to fund Piping Plover and shorebird research and conservation.

Copyright

Monty and Rose Nest at Montrose
Published by Tamima Itani, Monty and Rose, L.L.C.

Written by Tamima Itani
Edited by Anna-Maria Crum
Cover and book design by Anna-Maria Crum
Printed and bound by Bang Printing, Brainerd, Minnesota

ISBN 978-163821935-4

Visit plovermother.com for more information on Monty and Rose and their offspring.

Monty beat his wings faster. Any minute now he'd be with Rose. Last summer they had promised to meet at Montrose Beach to nest there.

A song filled his heart when he spotted the beach. "Pip-pip-pip-pip," he called to let Rose know he was back. But who was that other Piping Plover? A male! He was dancing for Rose!

Monty landed next to the bird. How dare he dance for Rose! “Rose is my mate!” Monty stood straight and tall. He puffed his chest to look twice as big.

The other male stopped dancing and stared. Monty refused to turn away and stared back with all his strength and power.

The intruder turned his head. He crouched, defeated, flapped his wings and flew off. Monty had won.

Monty puffed out his chest even more and started his high-stepping dance towards Rose. Tap, tap, tap; kicking up one leg high in the air after the other, very fast.

Rose flared her tail, showing Monty she was ready to start a family, too.

Monty kept up his dance, getting closer and closer. Soon he was right next to her. They snuggled close.

Monty scratched a nest. “How about here?”

“It’s too close to the walkway,” peeped Rose. “People could step on our eggs.”

Monty picked a place farther away from the people and made another nest.

Rose bobbed her head. This one was perfect. She sat on it and before long, there were four speckled eggs.

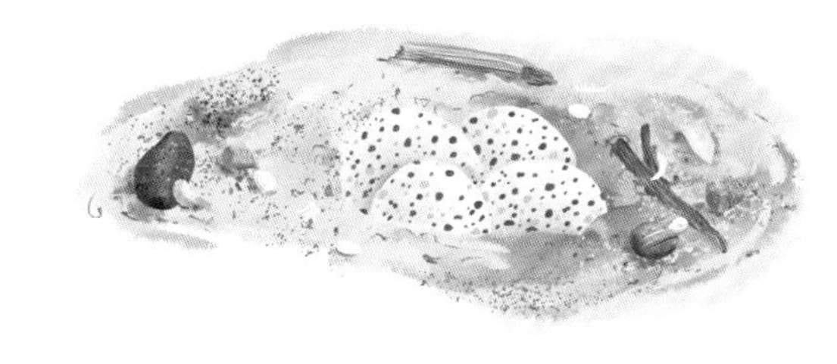

One day, a man put a cage over the nest.

Monty peeped and dragged his wing in the sand, pretending to be hurt to lure the man away.

"It's okay, Monty," peeped Rose. "I remember there was a cage over my nest when I was little. It kept the other eggs safe from coyotes and raccoons until they hatched, too."

One morning, a worried Rose looked up as lightning ripped the sky. Rain poured down in sheets. The waves crashed closer and closer until they reached the nest...and covered the eggs.

"We must go!" cried Rose.

The next morning, Rose and Monty stood on the boardwalk. "We've lost our nest two years in a row," peeped Monty. He didn't know what to do.

"I can lay four more eggs if you scrape me a new nest. We can still do it!" peeped Rose.

Monty quickly found a dry spot and scratched a new nest. Soon, Rose laid four new eggs.

Rose and Monty took turns keeping the eggs warm for four long weeks.

Finally, Rose felt movement. “Monty! Come quick.”

Monty rushed over and together they watched the egg wobble. “Crack!” A tiny beak poked through a hole. The beak chipped away, making the hole bigger and bigger. A large piece of shell flopped over. A baby chick’s head appeared! The egg tipped and the chick flopped out—rumpled and wet, its eyes barely open.

“Our first chick,” Rose peeped. She lovingly tucked the baby under her, while they waited for the other eggs to hatch. But the chick squirmed out from under her and took a few steps.

“Look at her go!” Monty peeped joyously!

Soon a second chick hatched, then a third. The fourth egg, though, remained still.

The three chicks were tiny—like little white clouds on twigs, with shiny eyes and black beaks. They scurried around, catching small sand bugs. Sometimes the chicks lost their balance and tumbled. But before Monty or Rose could rush to their side, they were back on their feet, running again. There were so many tiny bugs for them to catch and eat.

When the chicks got tired or were afraid, they'd run to Rose or Monty and cuddle under their bellies and wings. They made Mom or Dad look like a centipede with so many legs coming out of them.

One day, a bunch of gulls landed nearby. Rose peeped, “Monty!” as she ran at the gulls.

“Get away from our chicks!” peeped Monty.

Together, Monty and Rose kicked and beat at the big gulls with their wings and legs. Their fierceness worked and the gulls flew away.

The chicks were safe.

But the next morning, Monty spotted dogs running on the beach and coming straight at them! Dogs could snatch a chick in their teeth in no time.

"Pip, pip, pip!" warned Monty and Rose. The chicks immediately flattened in the sand, staying perfectly still. Eventually, the dogs were shooed away and the parents stopped piping. The chicks popped up from the sand.

Between people, dogs, and other birds, Rose and Monty were kept pretty busy.

One day, the chicks hopped across the sand, their little wings stretched as far as they could go.

Look, Rose," peeped Monty, "our chicks are trying to fly!"

But the little wings were too short to catch the air.

Monty and Rose giggled as they watched their chicks.

The summer grew old. Soon it would be fall.

"It's time for you to go south, Rose, and get strong for the coming winter," Monty peeped. "I'll watch over our chicks and keep them safe."

Rose didn't want to leave. She spent a lot of time with the chicks, brooding them under her wings and looking after them while they were feeding. She would miss them so much.

But she knew Monty was right. So, after eating as much as she could for the long flight ahead, she took one last look at her little family then flapped her wings, heading south for the winter.

Monty took very good care of the chicks. Day after day, the chicks tried to fly like Dad. They flapped their wings and hopped across the sand.

One day, a chick fell ill. There was nothing that Monty could do to make him feel better. The chick wouldn't eat or move. Monty brooded him for a long time.

A woman who had been on the beach every day and kept dogs and people away from them, walked gently up to him and said softly, "Monty, I have to take your baby to the zoo doctor. She will take good care of him."

Monty tried to lure her away from the chick by pretending his wing was broken. But his little chick needed help, so he let her take him.

Monty doubled his attention on the remaining two chicks, making sure they grew strong. One day, the oldest chick took off and flew from one end of the beach to the other. She was soon followed by her sibling.

Monty's chest puffed up bigger than he had ever felt it. His chicks were flying! His eyes followed their silhouettes against the white clouds and afternoon sun. Now that his chicks were flying, he knew they'd be all right, safe from the dogs or people or other animals that might go after them.

He didn't remember flapping his own wings, but soon Monty was flying next to his chicks, catching the currents over the water and riding them up into the bright blue sky.

Author's note

The Great Lakes Piping Plovers historically numbered 400 to 800 pairs prior to the 1800s. By 1983, that number had dropped to only 12 breeding pairs, located primarily in Michigan. The Great Lakes population was subsequently listed as federally endangered in 1985 and significant efforts were expanded to encourage population recovery. As of 2020, 64 pairs were recorded nesting in the Great Lakes region with the breeding range expanding to five states adjoining the Great Lakes in the U.S. and the province of Ontario in Canada.

In May 2018, a pair of Piping Plovers was observed exhibiting courtship behavior in the gravel parking lot at Waukegan Beach, Lake County, IL. One plover sported an orange band with a yellow dot on its lower left leg, a silver band on its upper right leg and a green band with the alphanumeric characters G202 on its lower right leg and was identified as plover -,O:X,G (Ydot, G202), a male plover that hatched in 2017 from a nest in Silver Lake State Park, MI. The other plover wore an orange band with a red dot on its lower left leg, a silver band on its upper right leg and a dark blue band with the alphanumeric characters B158 on its lower left leg. This plover was identified as -,O:X,B (Rdot, B158), a female that also hatched in 2017, but at Muskegon State Park, MI, a beach just south of where the male originated. In June 2018, this pair made a nesting attempt in the gravel parking lot. Unfortunately, it was determined that nest success was untenable due to its location. The nest was salvaged and the eggs taken to the University of Michigan Biological Station Captive Rearing Center near Pellston, MI where they were artificially incubated. One of the three chicks to hatch survived and was released to the wild.

In June 2019, the same pair nested at Montrose Beach, in Chicago, IL. It is then that I named them Monty and Rose, in the spur of the moment, to facilitate communication with others. Their first nest was lost when Montrose beach was flooded in a lake surge and the beach was under water for a few days. Monty and Rose chose a different, dryer location at Montrose, re-nested, and in August 2019, two chicks successfully fledged, ending a 71-yr absence of Piping Plovers breeding in Chicago and Cook County. Monty and Rose became local, state and national celebrities, with their story covered in multiple local, and some national, news outlets.

Nesting, hatching and fledging occurred in close proximity to the third largest metropolitan city in the country. Given the federal endangered status of these birds, an outpouring of agency support was expanded to include significant volunteer efforts to monitor and protect the plovers, their nest and offspring. I was proud to co-lead the coordination efforts of nearly 200 volunteers who spent hundreds of hours monitoring over a 13-week period and provided a unique observation window into the courting and breeding cycle of Piping Plovers in a highly dynamic environment where conflicts over recreational and public use often erupted.

Monty and Rose hold a special place in my heart. They were the first Piping Plovers I ever met, in their hatch year in 2017, at Waukegan Beach, when they were only a few weeks old. I am grateful to be part of their story and to be able to give them a voice.

For more information about Monty and Rose and their offspring, visit plovermother.com and chicagopipingplover.org.